# TOTALLY TWISTED PUZZLES

## DEFINITELY NOT FOR SLOTHS!

Hi, I'm Sloth. Keep an eye out for me as you work through this book!

You may have gathered that this is not a normal puzzle book - it's a TOTALLY TWISTED puzzle book.

Some puzzles are easy and some are hard but beware, things are not always what they seem! Keep your wits about you. You'll need all the wits you can get!

This book is definitely not for sloths, well, apart from me, but then I am TOTALLY TWISTED...

Before you start, check out the CHICKEN EGG CODE.
You'll need this for some of the puzzles but hey,
why not use it with your friends to send each other
top secret messages?

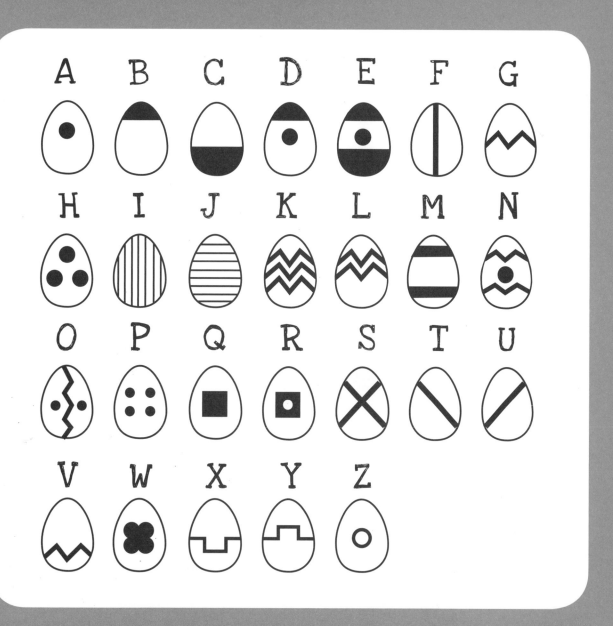

# THE HIDDEN ME

## Draw your portrait below.

Your name in
chicken egg code is

# DRAW YOUR DREAM VACATION HOUSE...

# DOES A HEADLESS DOG BARK?
## MATCH EACH HEAD WITH ITS BODY.

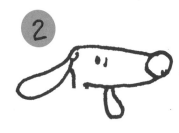

# WHAT'S HIDING IN THIS PICTURE?

# HOW many OWLS can you COUNT?

# DOODLE STOP!

No need to rush...

# How many stars in this pattern?

Color them in.

4

# CONNECT THE DOTS TO REVEAL WHAT'S IN THE WATER.

# SPOT THE DIFFERENCE?

## Finish these patterns of SMILING FACES.

1

2

3

# TIME FOR A QUICK DOODLE!

Hurry up! Tick, tock!

# Which piece is missing from this picture?

The pieces are upside down.

# Decode the chicken eggs to find the names of these three galactic giants!

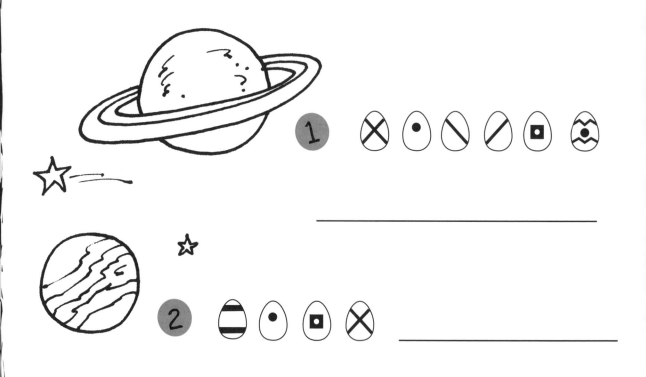

1

_____

2 _____

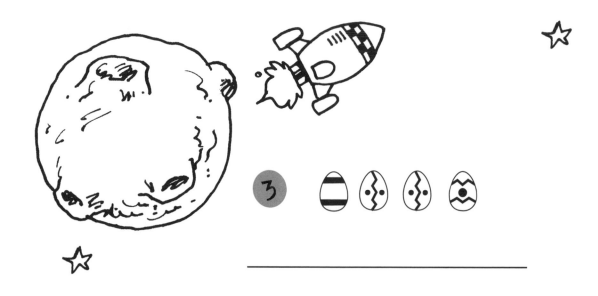

3

_____

# WHO IS THIS RABBIT LOOKING AT?

# WHICH IS THE WAY THROUGH THE MAZE?

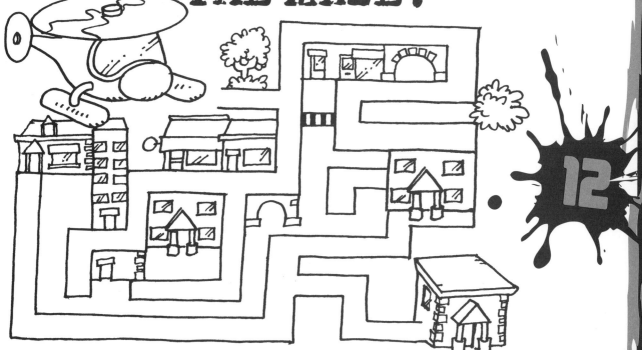

# DRAW A TOTALLY TWISTED DOODLE...

# CAN you SPOT the DIFFERENCES between these two pictures?

# COMPLETE THE PICTURE!

# DOODLE A DAYDREAM...

**...or daydream a doodle!**

# PUT the PIECES in the CORRECT order to MAKE a PICTURE of a BOY.

# Decode the colors and then color the pictures.

1  _____

2 _____

3 _____

4 _____

5 _____

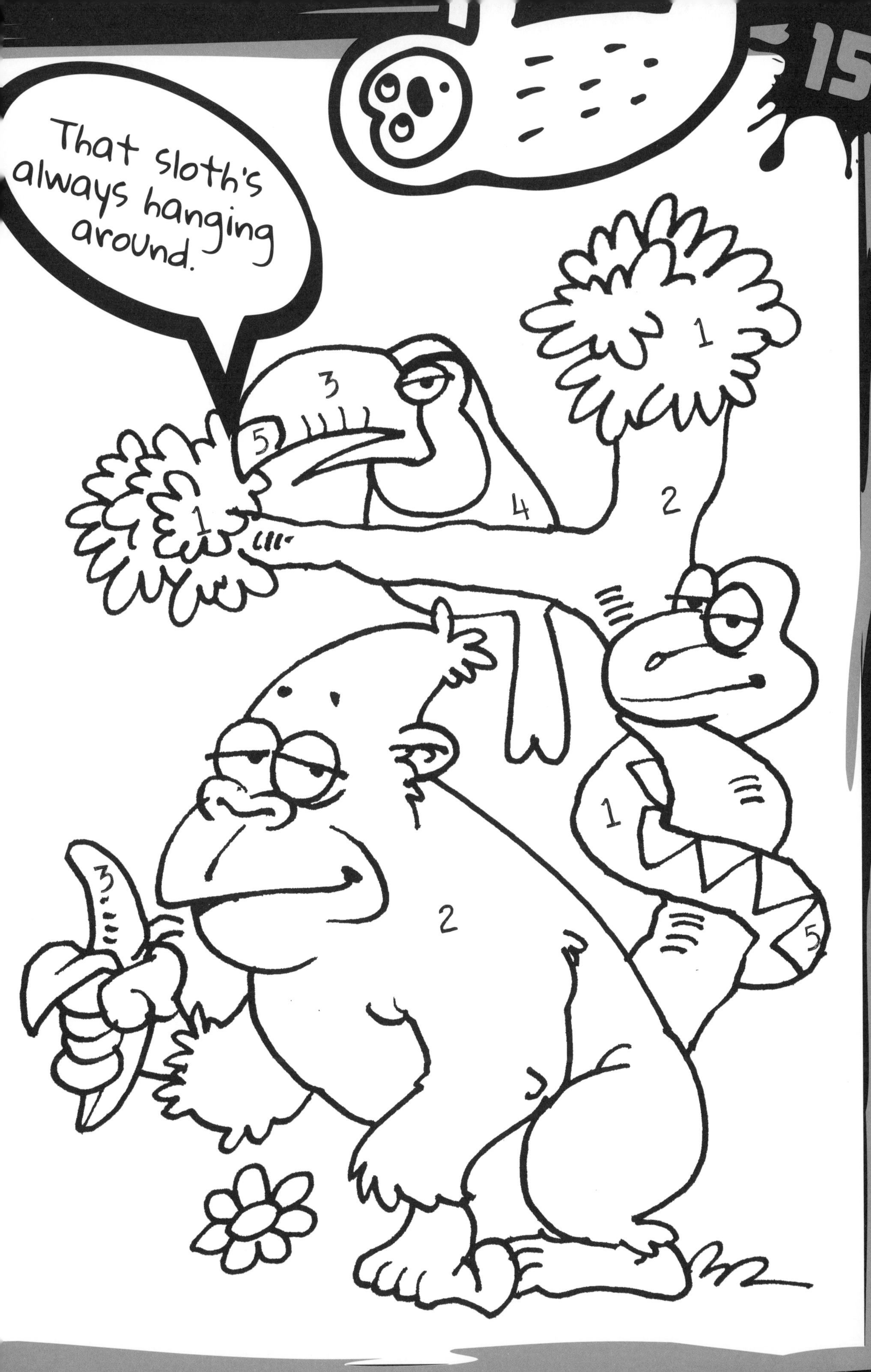
That sloth's always hanging around.
3
5
1
1
4
2
1
3
2
5

# Draw this dinosaur upside down!

ADD THE MISSING NUMBERS TO MAKE EACH TOTAL.

A) **10** − **5** + ___ = **8**

B) **20** − **5** + ___ = **21**

C) **45** − **5** + ___ = **45**

# MATCH THE SHADOW TO THE BiRD.

17

# DRAW YOURSELF AS A STAR!

## HOW many ACORNS can you COUNT?

18

# TAKE A BREAK.
# DRAW A DOODLE...

# HOW MANY DIFFERENCES BETWEEN THESE TWO PICTURES?

# FINISH DRAWING THIS DOG WITH YOUR EYES CLOSED.

# Draw lines to match the snake halves.

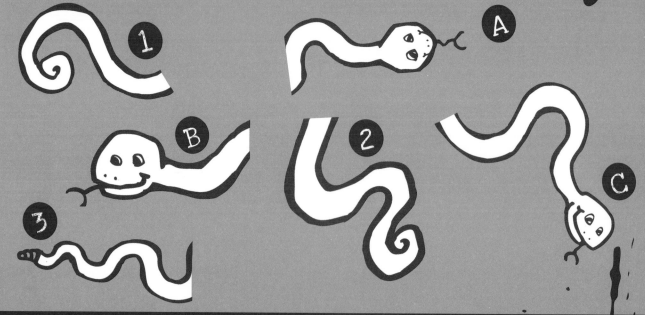

1

2

3

A

B

C

# WHICH ITEM is the ODD one out?

# WHICH PATH leads to the DOGHOUSE? WHAT is WRONG with this PICTURE?

# DRAW A DOODLE REALLY SLOOOWLYYY.

**This doodle took me..............minutes to draw.**

**Match the feet to the clowns.**

23

1
2
3
4

A
B
C
D

**what's WRONG with this picture?**

24

# CAN you FIND the PAIRS?

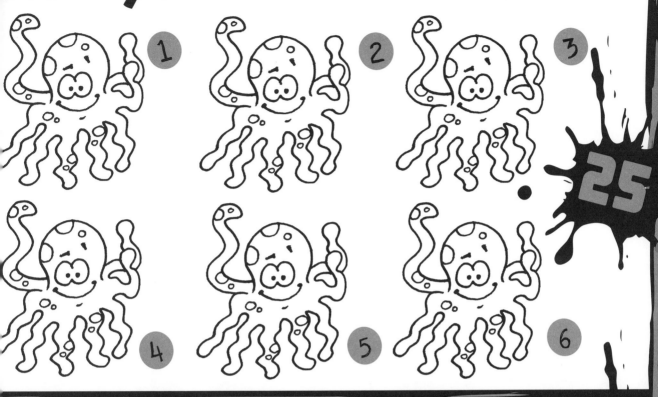

1
2
3

25

# What is this a shadow of?

26

Run!

# WHICH IS THE MISSING PIECE?

# DOODLE BREAK!

# Give these BIRDS their books back!

# How many SLUGS can you count?

PUT these PIECES in the RIGHT order to make the RABBIT upside down!

30

# 31

## Which totally twisted footwear belongs to which child?

# Connect the dots to reveal what this boy is doing.

# DOODLE WITH YOUR EYES CLOSED... DON'T FALL ASLEEP!

# Finish these DOMINO sequences.

A

B

C

# Look at these items for 60 seconds.

Now close your eyes and draw them on the opposite page.

**How many did you get?**

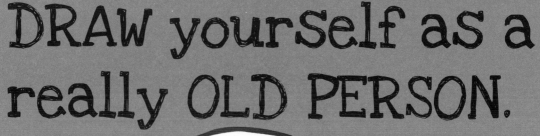

# DRAW yourself as a really OLD PERSON.

# WHAT THREE ANIMALS CAN YOU SEE HERE?

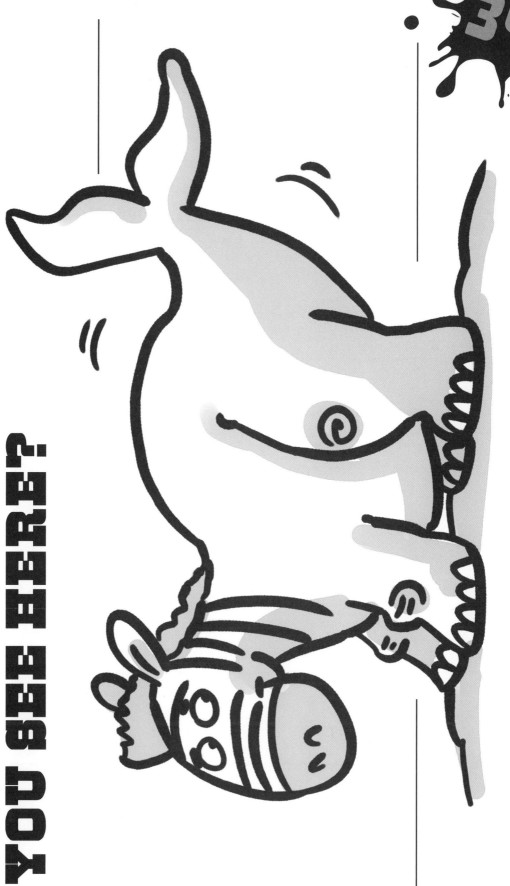

# DOODLE UPSIDE DOWN...

# HOW many SHAPES can you See here?

## ADD THE MISSING NUMBERS TO MAKE EACH TOTAL.

A    6   −   3   +   ⬚   =   12

B    36   −   9   +   ⬚   =   41

C    74   −   36   +   ⬚   =   66

# What's wrong with this lion?

37

HOW MANY PETALS ON THIS FLOWER?

38

# DOODLE BREAK!

# HOW MANY ARMADILLOS DO THESE PIECES MAKE?

# DRAW this KANGAROO
## using the hand you don't normally draw with.

# WHAT IS THIS?

Connect the dots to find out!

# What animals can you see here?

_____

_____

_____

## HOW many GHOSTS can you COUNT?

# GET CREATIVE,
# GET DOODLING...

# Draw yourself wearing this T-shirt.

# FINISH THE PATTERNS.

1
2
3
4

# Footloose and fancy free!

Match the shoes to the people!

1
2
3

A
B
C

# Dino dilemma!
## Which piece completes each dino?

# DRAW YOUR OWN DINOSAUR...

**My dinosaur is called** ........................

# Decode the names of these birds.

**Don't forget to use the chicken egg code!**

# HOW MANY NUMBERS CAN YOU SEE?

3 ☐   6 ☐   8 ☐

# DRAW A TOTALLY TWISTED DOODLE...

# WHAT ANIMALS CAN YOU SEE HERE ?

Draw your own mammal mash-up on the opposite page.

48

# HOW many SLOTHS can you see HANGING around the GARDEN?

49

# Draw yourself as a wizard.

shazzam!

# Match the shadow to the ghost.

# Last chance to doodle!

# ANSWERS

1 — 1-B, 2-C, 3-A.

2 — Nothing.

3 — 53       4 — 32

5 — A hippopotamus.

6 — One is a clown and one is a dog.

7 — 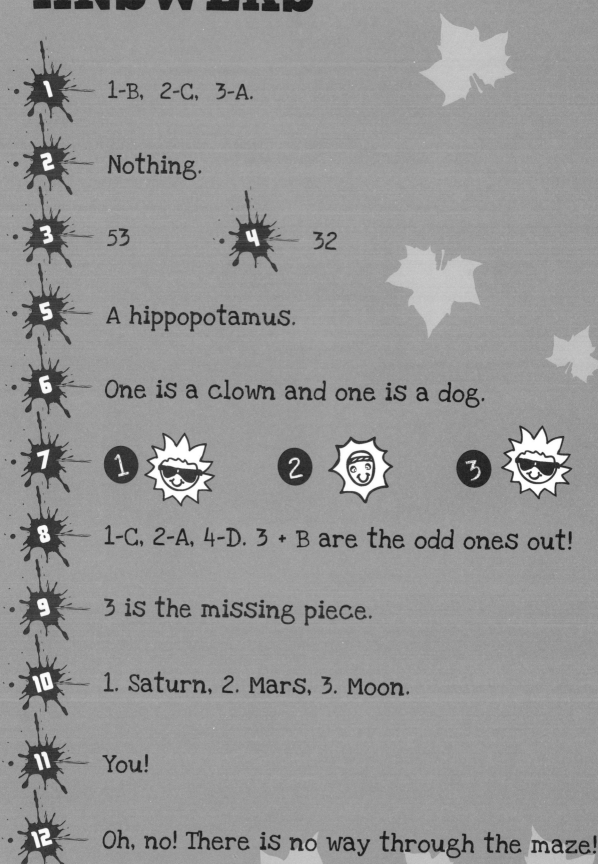 1    2    3

8 — 1-C, 2-A, 4-D. 3 + B are the odd ones out!

9 — 3 is the missing piece.

10 — 1. Saturn, 2. Mars, 3. Moon.

11 — You!

12 — Oh, no! There is no way through the maze!

**13** — There are none!

**14** — 3, 1, 2, 4.

**15** — 1. green,  2. brown,  3. yellow,  4. black,  5. red.

**16** — A-3,  B-6,  C-5.

**17** — Number 1 is the correct shadow.

**18** — 34 acorns.     **19** — None!

**20** — 1-C,  2-B,  3-A.

**21** — The paintbrush.

**22** — They all do! Giraffes don't live in doghouses!

**23** — 1-D,  2-A,  3-B,  4-C.

**24** The driver is looking the wrong way!

**25** There are none as they are all the same.

**26** A girl with a crab chasing a boy.

**27** Piece 3.

**28** 1-B, 2-A, 3-C.

**29** 26 slugs.

**30** 2, 3, 1, 5, 6, 4.

**31** 1-B, 2-C, 3-A.

**32** Windsurfing.

**33** Domino A-4/5, domino B-5/2, domino C-6/4.

**34** Front - zebra, middle - elephant, back - whale.

**35** ⬤ = 4  △ = 3  ◡ = 3  ◇ = 3  ⬡ = 0

**36** A-9, B-14, C-28.

**37** He doesn't have a mane!

**38** There are 56 petals.

**39** There are 5 armadillos.

**40** A pyramid!

**41** Top - dolphin, middle - crab, bottom - kangaroo.

**42** 35 ghosts.

**43**
1
2
3
4

**44** 1-B, 2-C, 3-A.

**45** 1-B, 2-C, 3-A.

**46** 1. ostrich, 2. flamingo, 3. blackbird.

**47** Number 3-11, number 6-10, number 8-9.

**48** Monkey, butterfly, and bear.

**49**  There are five sloths.

**50** Shadow C matches the ghost.

**51** Yawn! Time for a nap but check out your answers first!